To Michael, David and Chrissy – who love to
wreak havoc while Mum and Dad Snore On
– K.W.

For Alan Baker, my tutor
– J.C.

POCKET
BOOKS

An imprint of Simon & Schuster UK Ltd
Africa House, 64 - 78 Kingsway, London WC2B 6AH
First published in the USA in 2001 by Simon & Schuster Inc.
First published in Great Britain in 2001 by Simon & Schuster UK Ltd
Paperback edition published in 2002 by Pocket Books
Text copyright © 2001 by Karma Wilson
Illustrations copyright © 2001 by Jane Chapman
All rights reserved, including the right of reproduction in whole or in any form.
Book design by Ann Bobco.
The text of this book is set in Adobe Calson.
The illustrations were rendered in acrylic paint.
POCKET BOOKS and colophon are registered trademarks of Simon & Schuster
A CIP catalogue record for this book is available from the British Library

ISBN-10 : 07434 62092
ISBN-13 : 9780743462099

Printed in China

5 7 9 10 8 6 4

Bear Snores On

Karma Wilson

illustrations by Jane Chapman

POCKET
BOOKS

*I*n a cave, in the woods in his deep, dark lair, through the long, cold winter sleeps a great brown bear.

Cuddled in a heap, with his eyes shut tight, he sleeps through the day, he sleeps through the night.

The cold winds howl and the night sounds growl.

But
the bear
snores on.

An itty-bitty mouse-pitter-pat, tip-toe-creep-crawls
in the cave from the fluff-cold snow.

Mouse squeaks, "Too damp, too dank, too dark." So he lights wee twigs with a small, hot spark.

The coals pip-pop and the wind doesn't stop.

But
the bear
snores on.

Two glowing eyes sneak-peek in the den.
Mouse cries, "Who's there?" and a hare hops in.

"Ho Mouse!"
says Hare.
"Long time,
no see!"
So they pop
white corn.
And they brew
black tea.

Mouse sips wee slurps. Hare burps
big BURPS!

But
the bear
snores on.

A badger scuttles by, sniff-snuffs at the air.
"I smell yummy-yums! Perhaps we can share?

"I've brought honey-nuts," Badger says with a grin.
"Let's divvy them up, cosy down . . . and dig in!"

And they nibble and they munch with a

CHEW–

CHOMP–

CRUNCH!

But
the bear
snores on.

A gopher and a mole tunnel up through the floor.
Then a wren and a raven flutter in through the door!

Mole mutters, "What a night!"
"What a storm!" twitters Wren.
And everybody clutters in the great bear's den.

They tweet and they titter. They chat and they chitter.

But
the bear
snores on.

*I*n a cave, in the woods, a slumbering bear
sleeps through the party in his very own lair.

Hare stokes the fire. Mouse seasons stew.

Then a small pepper fleck makes the bear . . .

RAAAAA - CHOO

He blows and he sneezes,
and the whole crowd freezes . . .

And
the bear
WAKES UP!

BEAR GNARLS
and SNARLS.
BEAR ROARS
and he RUMBLES!
BEAR JUMPS
and he STOMPS.
BEAR GROWLS
and he GRUMBLES!

"you've sneaked into my lair
and you've all had fun!
but me? I was sleeping
and . . .

I've had none!"

And he whimpers and he
moans, he wails and he groans . . .

And the bear blubbers on!

Mouse squeaks, "Don't fret. Don't fuss. Look, see? We can pop more corn! We can brew more tea!"

Bear gulps. Bear gobbles. He sighs with
delight. Then he spins tall tales through
the blustery night.

When the sun peeks up on a crisp
clear dawn . . . Bear can't sleep,

But
his friends
snore on.